Hor(M)onology®
Menstrual Cycle Tracker Journal

Chart Your Mood, Health and Potential
Every Day of Your Cycle

Volume _____

Gabrielle Lichterman
author of *28 Days: What Your Cycle Reveals About Your Moods, Health and Potential*

Hor(M)onology
P R E S S

Published by Hormonology Press
St. Petersburg, Florida, USA

ISBN-13: 978-1-7345983-2-2

Hormonology® Menstrual Cycle Tracker Journal is intended as a reference volume only, not as a medical manual. In light of the complex, individual, and specific nature of health problems, this book is not intended to replace professional medical advice. The ideas, procedures, and suggestions in this book are intended to supplement, not replace, the advice of a trained medical professional. Consult with your physician before adopting the suggestions in this book, as well as about any condition that may require diagnosis or medical attention. The author and publisher disclaim any liability arising directly or indirectly from the use of this book.

This publication is designed to provide accurate and authoritative information with regard to the subject matter covered. It is sold with the understanding that the publisher is not engaged in rendering legal, accounting, or other professional advice. If legal advice or other expert assistance is required, the services of a competent professional should be sought.

—From a *Declaration of Principles* jointly adopted by a Committee of the American Bar Association and a Committee of Publishers and Associations

Hormonology® Menstrual Cycle Tracker Journal is not intended in any way to help you avoid pregnancy or become pregnant. Consult with your healthcare provider before starting any new health, diet, exercise, supplement or herb regimen.

For more information about this book and its author,
visit MyHormonology.com.

This book belongs to

_____

CONTENTS

Introduction
Menstrual cycle tracking for health and happiness

Thirty-five. That's the average number of years you'll have menstrual cycles in your lifetime. Starting from your tween years and continuing through graduation from secondary school, your first car, your first job, trade school, college, graduate school, marriage, your first house, military service, volunteer missions, motherhood, aunthood, work promotions, business launches, hard-fought competitions, dream vacations, mid-life career changes, planning for retirement and possibly even after becoming a grandmother or great-aunt.

Throughout all of these life events, you'll have a menstrual cycle. This typically means you'll be getting a period every month or so (if you have a uterus and aren't taking continuous hormone birth control).

It also means your hormones will be impacting you from the first day of your period through the day before your next period—and these hormonal influences will affect virtually every aspect of your life: your mood, energy, optimism, confidence, self-esteem, desire to socialize, memory, concentration, romantic attractions, libido, pain sensitivity, how you spend money, patience, resilience, willpower, health issues and much more.

Knowing what you can expect from your period and hormones helps you harness these effects: You'll know when you can capitalize on cycle-related benefits, such as when your mood and energy peak. And, you'll be able to prepare to overcome cycle-related challenges, for example, if you get intense menstrual cramps or when you're experiencing fatigue.

Using this *Hormonology® Menstrual Cycle Tracker Journal*—whether you have a natural cycle (no hormone birth control) or you take hormone birth control—is a vital way to discover, learn and understand how your period and hormones impact you. Then, you can predict and plan for these changes in future cycles.

Plus, there are lots more benefits. You'll be able to:

- Show your healthcare providers (doctor, therapist, dietitian, etc.) as a way to tailor treatment around your cycle or identify health issues
- Organize data that's important to you—such as mood, energy, desire to socialize or pain sensitivity—across your cycle

- Have a record of all the effects you typically experience so you can recognize when significant changes occur, which could possibly indicate a symptom of a health issue that needs to be addressed
- Determine which treatments for cycle-impacted conditions are working and which aren't
- Become familiar with the intensity and frequency of hormonal effects— and what changes them, such as following healthy habits or experiencing stress
- Get in tune with your body's own rhythms

Why paper period tracking?

In this digital age, there are dozens of menstrual cycle tracking mobile apps that help you keep tabs on what's going on with your cycle. Mine is among them. My Hormone Horoscope App was one of the first menstrual cycle tracker apps ever developed, and it broke ground as the only app to deliver a daily summary of how your hormones impact you every day.

So, why would I want you to use a *paper* cycle tracker? Several reasons:

- It's easier to see all the data you put into a book since you don't have to switch from screen to screen or scroll down on a small device
- It's easier to show your healthcare team charts and notes in a book than to find data scattered throughout an app
- You can do more with the data you enter, plus you can decide how you want to use it, such as making graphs and lists
- The data you enter won't be lost due to technology problems, for example, if your device breaks or the app company closes down
- Your information is as private as you want it to be (my Hormone Horoscope Apps are 100% private, however, many other menstrual cycle tracker apps do access, share and sell the personal data you put into them)

If you love the hormone information you get in my Hormone Horoscope App, or you want more details about hormonal effects in healthy, natural cycles (meaning no hormone birth control), you can find them in my book, **28 Days: What Your Cycle Reveals About Your Moods, Health and Potential** (available at Amazon). However, you do *not* need **28 Days** to use your **Hormonology® Menstrual Cycle Tracker Journal**. And, you can use this book whether your hormones are natural or you use hormone birth control. This means you can track your cycle in these pages starting today.

How to Use This Journal

The ***Hormonology® Menstrual Cycle Tracker Journal*** helps you understand what goes on during your cycle and how to make your cycle better. It does this by giving you 12 sets of comprehensive menstrual cycle trackers to monitor physical, emotional, health and other changes you experience from the first day of your period through the day before your next period. You also get 12 sets of six-page dot graphs, which help you organize your data. To get started:

1. Fill out your menstrual cycle tracker charts

In this book, you get 12 sets of menstrual cycle tracker charts for cycles lasting up to 50 days. With them you can:

- ✓ Keep track of period and ovulation dates
- ✓ Monitor your flow
- ✓ Monitor cervical mucus changes
- ✓ Rate cycle-related general symptoms
- ✓ Rate cycle-related health symptoms
- ✓ Rate cycle-related emotional changes
- ✓ Customize charts by adding topics you want to track
- ✓ Add additional notes, such as appointments or medications

> **TIP:** *Use a pen with erasable ink or a pencil to fill out this journal. This way, if your answers shift over time or you need to correct data, you can easily makes changes.*

To use the menstrual cycle tracker charts, start with the first set and fill it out every day as you go through your cycle. Rank categories by using numbers (1 to 10), shading in the boxes or coming up with your own ranking method that works best for you. Once you get your next period, this indicates Day 1 of a new cycle. So, you then start filling out the next set of menstrual cycle tracker charts.

To figure out where you are in your cycle, read the "Menstrual Cycle Know-How" chapter. Don't get a period because you don't have a uterus? If you have fully functioning ovaries, pinpointing ovulation can help keep you on track. Learn more in the "Menstrual Cycle Know-How" chapter.

Use the Notes section to add other details, such as if you're experiencing a major stressor that month (for example, moving to a new town). Or, use it to track changes that aren't easily ranked, such as recovery from an injury or surgery, training for an athletic event or noticing the type of person you're romantically attracted to across your cycle.

2. Graph your results

After each set of menstrual cycle tracker charts, there is a six-page set of blank dot graph pages. You can use the aligned dots as guidelines to shape cycle-related information into lists, graphs, logs, indexes, collections and more. This popular way of organizing information in a useful and creative way was invented by Ryder Carroll, author of **The Bullet Journal Method**.

Here are a couple of examples of ways you can use your cycle information in your dot graph pages:

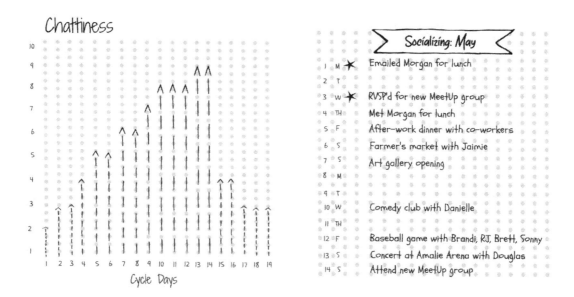

There are many other ways to use your dot graph pages. For inspiration, I recommend reading Carroll's book and visiting his website, BulletJournal.com.

2. Start a new volume

The **Hormonology® Menstrual Cycle Tracker Journal** enables you to track 12 consecutive menstrual cycles. The first book will be Volume 1 in your collection. Once all of these menstrual cycle trackers are filled out, you'll get a new **Hormonology® Menstrual Cycle Tracker Journal** and begin filling that out. That will be your Volume 2. After that's filled up, you'll move on to Volume 3, and so on.

Write the volume number on the spine, cover and title page so you can easily store and keep track of the history of your cycles. You may want to refer back to this vital information due to changes in health, when noticing shifts as you age, to figure out when you resume a pattern that's typical for you after pregnancy or discontinuing hormone birth control, or for another reason.

Menstrual Cycle Know-How

Where are you in your cycle?

To fill in your menstrual cycle tracker charts, you'll need some basics about your cycle. For starters, here's how to know where you are in your cycle:

When your cycle starts

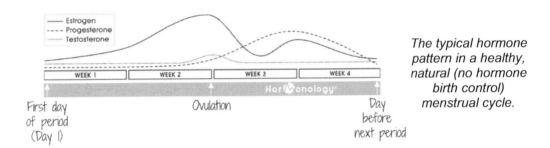

The typical hormone pattern in a healthy, natural (no hormone birth control) menstrual cycle.

      Day 1 is the first day of your period. Your period can be light or heavy, but the first day you see red is your Day 1. That's because it means your body's level of estrogen has dropped low enough to signal menstruation. In a natural cycle (no hormone birth control), it also means that estrogen will begin rising again that day, in fact, just a few hours after your period begins.

      The day after Day 1 is Day 2 of your cycle. The day after that is Day 3 of your cycle, and so on.

      Your entire menstrual cycle lasts from the first day of your period (Day 1) through the day before your next period. The day you get your next period is Day 1 of a new menstrual cycle. Then you start counting all over again.

First half of your cycle

      For women with natural cycles and who ovulate, Day 1 through ovulation is the first half of your cycle. This is the "follicular" phase, which gets its name from the follicle that matures in your ovary during this time.

The first half of a natural cycle can vary in length. In fact, the length of this phase typically determines how long your *entire* cycle will be. This means if you have a cycle that's shorter than 28 days, it's because the follicular phase of your cycle was shorter than 14 days. If you have a cycle that's longer than 28 days, it's because this phase of your cycle was longer than 14 days.

Second half of your cycle

The day after ovulation marks the second half of your cycle—the "luteal" phase. It gets this name from a substance in the ovary that's left behind after ovulation called the *corpus luteum* (Latin for "yellow body"), which produces the hormone progesterone.

Your luteal phase is typically a stable number of days. That's because once ovulation occurs, a clock inside your body begins to tick down either to your period or pregnancy. If you didn't get pregnant, then you go on to get your period. For most women, this phase is 14 days long. However, the luteal phase can be slightly shorter or longer, but it's usually still a stable set number of days. Tracking your cycle can help you pinpoint your luteal phase length.

What this means for you

Once you pinpoint the day you ovulate, you'll count down 14 days (or the number of days in your luteal phase if it's different). The day after that is when you'll get your next period.

Important: There are factors that can alter the length your cycle, such as stress, some medications and certain health conditions. So, the above information is only a general guideline. Tracking your cycle can help you uncover which factors may impact your cycle length.

The difference between "Days" and "Weeks" in a cycle

For the purposes of Hormonology, I use both "Days" and "Weeks" to refer to where you are in a healthy, natural menstrual cycle.

The "Day" you're on refers to how many days it's been since the first day of your period. Day 1 is the day you get your period. Day 2 is the day after that. Day 3 is the day after that. And, so on. The "Week" you're on refers to the *hormonal phase* you're in. Even though I use the word "Week", these phases don't last the traditional seven days. The four Weeks break down like this:

- **Week 1:** The first seven days of your cycle—Day 1 (start of your period) to Day 7. Estrogen begins at its lowest point and slowly rises.
- **Week 2:** Day 8 through ovulation (which is typically Day 14 in a 28-day cycle). Estrogen rises until it peaks. Testosterone rises slightly at the end of Week 2 during ovulation. For Hormonology, Week 2 is the only phase that varies in length.

- **Week 3:** This phase spans the eight days following ovulation (which is Day 15 through Day 22 in a 28-day cycle). Estrogen and testosterone drop during the first three days and estrogen rises again for the rest of this cycle week. Progesterone rises steadily throughout your Week 3.
- **Week 4:** This phase spans the final six days of your cycle (which is Day 23 to Day 28 in a 28-day cycle). Your Week 4 is commonly known as your premenstrual phase. Estrogen and progesterone drop throughout.

I developed these four "Week" categories for Hormonology as a shortcut to figure out where you are in your cycle and what's going on with you hormonally. Each Week has its own "personality" because of the hormone levels and hormone changes going on within it. This makes it easy to know in an instant what to expect simply by knowing which Week you're in. For example, if you're in your Week 1, you'll know that your energy starts off low, but it's increasing day by day. If you're in your Week 2, you'll know that your energy is peaking. If you're in your Week 3, you'll know that your energy is hitting bottom. If you're in your Week 4, you'll know that your energy is getting slightly better than it was in your Week 3, but it's still low compared to Week 2.

You can learn more about how your natural hormones impact your mood, health and behavior every day of your cycle in my book, ***28 Days: What Your Cycle Reveals About Your Moods, Health and Potential*** and at MyHormonology.com.

How to determine when you ovulate

To figure out when you ovulate, there are certain physical symptoms you can look for, which include feeling pain in either ovary (called "mittelschmerz", which is German for "middle pain") and seeing slippery vaginal fluid that resembles raw egg white. However, there are ovulation detection tools (available at drugstores and online) that are more reliable. These include:

- **Basal thermometer:** It detects a subtle increase in your basal (lowest) body temperature that occurs at ovulation due to rising progesterone. To use: Take your temperature every day once you wake up, but before you get out of bed. An increase in temperature of one-half to one degree in the middle of your cycle is a sign that you're ovulating.
- **Ovulation test strips:** These measure the level of luteinizing hormone (LH) that surges one to one-and-a-half days before ovulation. To use: Pass the strip through your urine and if it shows the level of your LH is peaking, you'll be ovulating within 24 to 36 hours.
- **Ovulation microscope:** This lipstick-sized microscope measures the level of salt in your saliva, which peaks at ovulation. To use: Dab saliva on the lens, let dry, then look through the microscope. If you see dots, you're not near ovulation. Dots and lines mean you're nearing ovulation. A fern pattern indicates you're very close to or are ovulating.

Important: Please do not use the information about ovulation or menstrual cycles in this book as a sole form of pregnancy prevention. If you do not use birth control (such as condoms), you can get pregnant on the days leading up to, the day of and the day after ovulation. That's because sperm can survive within your body for up to five days and your egg can survive up to 48 hours. Plus, your ovulation date could have changed due to a number of factors, such as stress, certain medications or illness.

If you're interested in using the natural family planning method—which relies on your body's cues to determine your fertile days—please seek training from a qualified natural family planning instructor.

What if you're taking hormone birth control?

If you take hormone birth control in the form of a pill, patch, ring, shot, implant or IUD, your hormones follow a different pattern than when your hormones are natural (no hormone birth control). There is a wide variation in what those hormone patterns are depending on the type of birth control, but generally speaking, you'll have a "flatter" cycle—meaning, you won't experience the high peaks of Week 2 when estrogen normally spikes. And, you may have a less intense and/or shorter premenstrual phase, which are the days when estrogen and progesterone fall in a natural cycle.

But, no matter which hormone birth control you use, this journal can be a valuable tool that helps you understand how these supplemental hormones impact you day to day.

What if you have ovaries, but do not have a uterus?

If your ovaries are fully functioning and you ovulate, but you don't have a uterus, your hormones likely follow an up-and-down pattern similar to someone who does have a uterus. This means you can track hormonal effects and determine where you are in your cycle even without a monthly period. To do so, you'll be using your ovulation date as a guidepost. You can pinpoint ovulation by using the ovulation detection tools I listed. Once you get the sign that you're ovulating, then the next day you'll be entering your luteal phase, which is typically 14 days long. The day following that phase would be your Day 1, indicating the start of a new menstrual cycle.

What if you have a medical condition that impacts hormones?

If you have a medical condition that makes your hormone pattern different from a healthy, natural cycle—for example, polycystic ovarian syndrome—you'll likely still find this journal useful. It can help you pinpoint patterns unique to your cycle, identify which treatments are or are not working and provide you with a collection of useful data to share with your healthcare providers.

HorMonology®
Menstrual Cycle Tracker Journal

How to use:

1 Fill out the menstrual cycle tracker charts every day as you go through your cycle. (To figure out where you are in your cycle, read the "Menstrual Cycle Know-How" chapter.)

2 Rank categories by using numbers (1 to 10), shading in the boxes or coming up with your own ranking method that works best for you.

3 Add categories of your own to track.

4 Use the Notes section to add other details, such as if you're experiencing a major event (for example, moving to a new town) or taking a new medication. Or use it to track topics that aren't easily ranked, such as recovery from an injury.

5 Use the dot graph pages to shape your data, for example, by creating lists or graphs.

6 Once you get your next period, this indicates Day 1 of a new cycle. When that happens, start filling out the next set of menstrual cycle tracker charts. (Have ovaries, but no uterus, so you don't bleed? Read the "Menstrual Cycle Know-How" chapter to learn how to track your cycle.)

Tip: Use an erasable pen or pencil to make it easier to correct or change data you input.

Cycle Dates

_____ to

_____

Menstrual Cycle Tracker #1

Flow: ☐ = none ⊡ = spotting ▭ = light ◪ = moderate ◼ = heavy

Cervical Mucus: D = dry, **S** = sticky, **C** = creamy, **W** = watery, **EW** = egg white, ____ = _____

DATE																									
CYCLE DAY	1	2	3	4	5	6	7	8	9	10	11	12	13	14	15	16	17	18	19	20	21	22	23	24	25
Flow/cervical mucus																									
# of products or cup rinses																									
Basal temp																									
Ovulation																									

General Symptoms

0=none, 1=low, 5=moderate, 10=high OR ☐ = none ▭ = low ◪ = moderate ◼ = high

CYCLE DAY	1	2	3	4	5	6	7	8	9	10	11	12	13	14	15	16	17	18	19	20	21	22	23	24	25
Acne																									
Appetite																									
Breast pain																									
Cramps																									
Fatigue																									
Fluid retention																									
Food cravings																									
Gas																									
Headache																									
Migraine																									
Nausea																									
Pain intensity																									
Sadness																									
Sleep issues																									
Stool: hard																									
Stool: loose																									
Urination																									
Worry																									

Menstrual Cycle Tracker #1

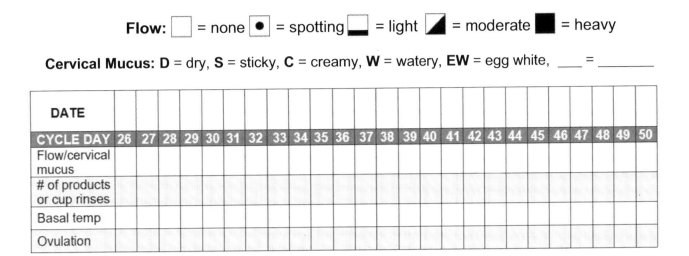

Flow: ☐ = none ⊡ = spotting ◲ = light ◩ = moderate ◼ = heavy

Cervical Mucus: D = dry, **S** = sticky, **C** = creamy, **W** = watery, **EW** = egg white, ____ = _____

DATE																									
CYCLE DAY	26	27	28	29	30	31	32	33	34	35	36	37	38	39	40	41	42	43	44	45	46	47	48	49	50
Flow/cervical mucus																									
# of products or cup rinses																									
Basal temp																									
Ovulation																									

General Symptoms

0=none, 1=low, 5=moderate, 10=high OR ☐ = none ◲ = low ◩ = moderate ◼ = high

CYCLE DAY	26	27	28	29	30	31	32	33	34	35	36	37	38	39	40	41	42	43	44	45	46	47	48	49	50
Acne																									
Appetite																									
Breast pain																									
Cramps																									
Fatigue																									
Fluid retention																									
Food cravings																									
Gas																									
Headache																									
Migraine																									
Nausea																									
Pain intensity																									
Sadness																									
Sleep issues																									
Stool: hard																									
Stool: loose																									
Urination																									
Worry																									

Medical Condition Symptoms

0=none, 1=low, 5=moderate, 10=high OR ☐ = none ◻ = low ◢ = moderate ■ = high

CYCLE DAY	1	2	3	4	5	6	7	8	9	10	11	12	13	14	15	16	17	18	19	20	21	22	23	24	25
Allergies																									
Anxiety																									
Asthma																									
Depression																									
Dry eye																									
Eczema																									
Endometriosis																									
Epilepsy																									
Fibromyalgia																									
GERD																									
IBS																									
Mania																									
MS																									
OCD																									
PCOS																									
PMDD																									
Social anxiety																									

Other Medical Condition Symptoms

0=none, 1=low, 5=moderate, 10=high OR ☐ = none ◻ = low ◢ = moderate ■ = high

CYCLE DAY	1	2	3	4	5	6	7	8	9	10	11	12	13	14	15	16	17	18	19	20	21	22	23	24	25

Medical Condition Symptoms

0=none, 1=low, 5=moderate, 10=high OR ☐ = none ◪ = low ◩ = moderate ■ = high

CYCLE DAY	26	27	28	29	30	31	32	33	34	35	36	37	38	39	40	41	42	43	44	45	46	47	48	49	50
Allergies																									
Anxiety																									
Asthma																									
Depression																									
Dry eye																									
Eczema																									
Endometriosis																									
Epilepsy																									
Fibromyalgia																									
GERD																									
IBS																									
Mania																									
MS																									
OCD																									
PCOS																									
PMDD																									
Social anxiety																									

Other Medical Condition Symptoms

0=none, 1=low, 5=moderate, 10=high OR ☐ = none ◪ = low ◩ = moderate ■ = high

CYCLE DAY	26	27	28	29	30	31	32	33	34	35	36	37	38	39	40	41	42	43	44	45	46	47	48	49	50

Mood, Body, Brain

0=none, 1=low, 5=moderate, 10=high OR ☐ = none ▁ = low ◣ = moderate ■ = high

CYCLE DAY	1	2	3	4	5	6	7	8	9	10	11	12	13	14	15	16	17	18	19	20	21	22	23	24	25
Ambition																									
Brainstorming																									
Chattiness																									
Concentration																									
Confidence																									
Courage																									
Creativity																									
Crushes																									
Energy																									
Extroversion																									
Humor/playful																									
Impulsivity																									
Introversion																									
Irritability																									
Libido																									
Memory																									
Money spent																									
Mood: general																									
Optimism																									
Orgasm																									
Patience																									
Productivity																									
Resilience																									
Risk-taking																									
Ruminating																									
Self-image																									
Skepticism																									
Socializing																									
Stress																									
Thinking speed																									
Verbal skills																									
Wanderlust																									
Willpower																									

Mood, Body, Brain

0=none, 1=low, 5=moderate, 10=high OR ☐ = none ◻ = low ◪ = moderate ■ = high

CYCLE DAY	26	27	28	29	30	31	32	33	34	35	36	37	38	39	40	41	42	43	44	45	46	47	48	49	50
Ambition																									
Brainstorming																									
Chattiness																									
Concentration																									
Confidence																									
Courage																									
Creativity																									
Crushes																									
Energy																									
Extroversion																									
Humor/playful																									
Impulsivity																									
Introversion																									
Irritability																									
Libido																									
Memory																									
Money spent																									
Mood: general																									
Optimism																									
Orgasm																									
Patience																									
Productivity																									
Resilience																									
Risk-taking																									
Ruminating																									
Self-image																									
Skepticism																									
Socializing																									
Stress																									
Thinking speed																									
Verbal skills																									
Wanderlust																									
Willpower																									

Other Mood, Body, Brain

0=none, 1=low, 5=moderate, 10=high OR ☐ = none ⬓ = low ◢ = moderate ■ = high

CYCLE DAY	1	2	3	4	5	6	7	8	9	10	11	12	13	14	15	16	17	18	19	20	21	22	23	24	25

NOTES:

Other Mood, Body, Brain

0=none, 1=low, 5=moderate, 10=high OR ☐ = none ▆ = low ◪ = moderate ■ = high

CYCLE DAY	26	27	28	29	30	31	32	33	34	35	36	37	38	39	40	41	42	43	44	45	46	47	48	49	50

NOTES:

Menstrual Cycle Tracker #2

Flow: ☐ = none ◉ = spotting ◻ = light ◩ = moderate ■ = heavy

Cervical Mucus: D = dry, **S** = sticky, **C** = creamy, **W** = watery, **EW** = egg white, ____ = _____

DATE																								
CYCLE DAY	1	2	3	4	5	6	7	8	9	10	11	12	13	14	15	16	17	18	19	20	21	22	23	24	25
Flow/cervical mucus																									
# of products or cup rinses																									
Basal temp																									
Ovulation																									

General Symptoms

0=none, 1=low, 5=moderate, 10=high OR ☐ = none ◻ = low ◩ = moderate ■ = high

CYCLE DAY	1	2	3	4	5	6	7	8	9	10	11	12	13	14	15	16	17	18	19	20	21	22	23	24	25
Acne																									
Appetite																									
Breast pain																									
Cramps																									
Fatigue																									
Fluid retention																									
Food cravings																									
Gas																									
Headache																									
Migraine																									
Nausea																									
Pain intensity																									
Sadness																									
Sleep issues																									
Stool: hard																									
Stool: loose																									
Urination																									
Worry																									

Menstrual Cycle Tracker #2

Flow: ☐ = none ⊡ = spotting ◲ = light ◸ = moderate ■ = heavy

Cervical Mucus: D = dry, **S** = sticky, **C** = creamy, **W** = watery, **EW** = egg white, ____ = _____

DATE																									
CYCLE DAY	26	27	28	29	30	31	32	33	34	35	36	37	38	39	40	41	42	43	44	45	46	47	48	49	50
Flow/cervical mucus																									
# of products or cup rinses																									
Basal temp																									
Ovulation																									

General Symptoms

0=none, 1=low, 5=moderate, 10=high OR ☐ = none ◲ = low ◸ = moderate ■ = high

CYCLE DAY	26	27	28	29	30	31	32	33	34	35	36	37	38	39	40	41	42	43	44	45	46	47	48	49	50
Acne																									
Appetite																									
Breast pain																									
Cramps																									
Fatigue																									
Fluid retention																									
Food cravings																									
Gas																									
Headache																									
Migraine																									
Nausea																									
Pain intensity																									
Sadness																									
Sleep issues																									
Stool: hard																									
Stool: loose																									
Urination																									
Worry																									

Medical Condition Symptoms

0=none, 1=low, 5=moderate, 10=high OR ☐ = none ◰ = low ◩ = moderate ◼ = high

CYCLE DAY	1	2	3	4	5	6	7	8	9	10	11	12	13	14	15	16	17	18	19	20	21	22	23	24	25
Allergies																									
Anxiety																									
Asthma																									
Depression																									
Dry eye																									
Eczema																									
Endometriosis																									
Epilepsy																									
Fibromyalgia																									
GERD																									
IBS																									
Mania																									
MS																									
OCD																									
PCOS																									
PMDD																									
Social anxiety																									

Other Medical Condition Symptoms

0=none, 1=low, 5=moderate, 10=high OR ☐ = none ◰ = low ◩ = moderate ◼ = high

CYCLE DAY	1	2	3	4	5	6	7	8	9	10	11	12	13	14	15	16	17	18	19	20	21	22	23	24	25

Medical Condition Symptoms

0=none, 1=low, 5=moderate, 10=high OR ☐ = none ▱ = low ◣ = moderate ■ = high

CYCLE DAY	26	27	28	29	30	31	32	33	34	35	36	37	38	39	40	41	42	43	44	45	46	47	48	49	50
Allergies																									
Anxiety																									
Asthma																									
Depression																									
Dry eye																									
Eczema																									
Endometriosis																									
Epilepsy																									
Fibromyalgia																									
GERD																									
IBS																									
Mania																									
MS																									
OCD																									
PCOS																									
PMDD																									
Social anxiety																									

Other Medical Condition Symptoms

0=none, 1=low, 5=moderate, 10=high OR ☐ = none ▱ = low ◣ = moderate ■ = high

CYCLE DAY	26	27	28	29	30	31	32	33	34	35	36	37	38	39	40	41	42	43	44	45	46	47	48	49	50

Mood, Body, Brain

0=none, 1=low, 5=moderate, 10=high OR ☐ = none ▭ = low ◢ = moderate ■ = high

CYCLE DAY	1	2	3	4	5	6	7	8	9	10	11	12	13	14	15	16	17	18	19	20	21	22	23	24	25
Ambition																									
Brainstorming																									
Chattiness																									
Concentration																									
Confidence																									
Courage																									
Creativity																									
Crushes																									
Energy																									
Extroversion																									
Humor/playful																									
Impulsivity																									
Introversion																									
Irritability																									
Libido																									
Memory																									
Money spent																									
Mood: general																									
Optimism																									
Orgasm																									
Patience																									
Productivity																									
Resilience																									
Risk-taking																									
Ruminating																									
Self-image																									
Skepticism																									
Socializing																									
Stress																									
Thinking speed																									
Verbal skills																									
Wanderlust																									
Willpower																									

Mood, Body, Brain

0=none, 1=low, 5=moderate, 10=high OR ☐ = none ◲ = low ◸ = moderate ■ = high

CYCLE DAY	26	27	28	29	30	31	32	33	34	35	36	37	38	39	40	41	42	43	44	45	46	47	48	49	50
Ambition																									
Brainstorming																									
Chattiness																									
Concentration																									
Confidence																									
Courage																									
Creativity																									
Crushes																									
Energy																									
Extroversion																									
Humor/playful																									
Impulsivity																									
Introversion																									
Irritability																									
Libido																									
Memory																									
Money spent																									
Mood: general																									
Optimism																									
Orgasm																									
Patience																									
Productivity																									
Resilience																									
Risk-taking																									
Ruminating																									
Self-image																									
Skepticism																									
Socializing																									
Stress																									
Thinking speed																									
Verbal skills																									
Wanderlust																									
Willpower																									

Other Mood, Body, Brain

0=none, 1=low, 5=moderate, 10=high OR ☐ = none ☐ = low ◢ = moderate ■ = high

CYCLE DAY	1	2	3	4	5	6	7	8	9	10	11	12	13	14	15	16	17	18	19	20	21	22	23	24	25

NOTES:

Other Mood, Body, Brain

0=none, 1=low, 5=moderate, 10=high OR ☐ = none ☐ = low ◣ = moderate ◼ = high

CYCLE DAY	26	27	28	29	30	31	32	33	34	35	36	37	38	39	40	41	42	43	44	45	46	47	48	49	50

NOTES:

Menstrual Cycle Tracker #3

Flow: ☐ = none ◉ = spotting ◪ = light ◩ = moderate ■ = heavy

Cervical Mucus: D = dry, **S** = sticky, **C** = creamy, **W** = watery, **EW** = egg white, ____ = _____

DATE																									
CYCLE DAY	1	2	3	4	5	6	7	8	9	10	11	12	13	14	15	16	17	18	19	20	21	22	23	24	25
Flow/cervical mucus																									
# of products or cup rinses																									
Basal temp																									
Ovulation																									

General Symptoms

0=none, 1=low, 5=moderate, 10=high OR ☐ = none ◪ = low ◩ = moderate ■ = high

CYCLE DAY	1	2	3	4	5	6	7	8	9	10	11	12	13	14	15	16	17	18	19	20	21	22	23	24	25
Acne																									
Appetite																									
Breast pain																									
Cramps																									
Fatigue																									
Fluid retention																									
Food cravings																									
Gas																									
Headache																									
Migraine																									
Nausea																									
Pain intensity																									
Sadness																									
Sleep issues																									
Stool: hard																									
Stool: loose																									
Urination																									
Worry																									

Menstrual Cycle Tracker #3

Flow: ☐ = none ⊡ = spotting ◪ = light ◩ = moderate ■ = heavy

Cervical Mucus: D = dry, **S** = sticky, **C** = creamy, **W** = watery, **EW** = egg white, ___ = _____

DATE																									
CYCLE DAY	26	27	28	29	30	31	32	33	34	35	36	37	38	39	40	41	42	43	44	45	46	47	48	49	50
Flow/cervical mucus																									
# of products or cup rinses																									
Basal temp																									
Ovulation																									

General Symptoms

0=none, 1=low, 5=moderate, 10=high OR ☐ = none ◪ = low ◩ = moderate ■ = high

CYCLE DAY	26	27	28	29	30	31	32	33	34	35	36	37	38	39	40	41	42	43	44	45	46	47	48	49	50
Acne																									
Appetite																									
Breast pain																									
Cramps																									
Fatigue																									
Fluid retention																									
Food cravings																									
Gas																									
Headache																									
Migraine																									
Nausea																									
Pain intensity																									
Sadness																									
Sleep issues																									
Stool: hard																									
Stool: loose																									
Urination																									
Worry																									

Medical Condition Symptoms

0=none, 1=low, 5=moderate, 10=high OR ☐ = none ☐ = low ◢ = moderate ■ = high

CYCLE DAY	1	2	3	4	5	6	7	8	9	10	11	12	13	14	15	16	17	18	19	20	21	22	23	24	25
Allergies																									
Anxiety																									
Asthma																									
Depression																									
Dry eye																									
Eczema																									
Endometriosis																									
Epilepsy																									
Fibromyalgia																									
GERD																									
IBS																									
Mania																									
MS																									
OCD																									
PCOS																									
PMDD																									
Social anxiety																									

Other Medical Condition Symptoms

0=none, 1=low, 5=moderate, 10=high OR ☐ = none ☐ = low ◢ = moderate ■ = high

CYCLE DAY	1	2	3	4	5	6	7	8	9	10	11	12	13	14	15	16	17	18	19	20	21	22	23	24	25

Medical Condition Symptoms

0=none, 1=low, 5=moderate, 10=high OR ☐ = none ▄ = low ◢ = moderate ■ = high

CYCLE DAY	26	27	28	29	30	31	32	33	34	35	36	37	38	39	40	41	42	43	44	45	46	47	48	49	50
Allergies																									
Anxiety																									
Asthma																									
Depression																									
Dry eye																									
Eczema																									
Endometriosis																									
Epilepsy																									
Fibromyalgia																									
GERD																									
IBS																									
Mania																									
MS																									
OCD																									
PCOS																									
PMDD																									
Social anxiety																									

Other Medical Condition Symptoms

0=none, 1=low, 5=moderate, 10=high OR ☐ = none ▄ = low ◢ = moderate ■ = high

CYCLE DAY	26	27	28	29	30	31	32	33	34	35	36	37	38	39	40	41	42	43	44	45	46	47	48	49	50

Mood, Body, Brain

0=none, 1=low, 5=moderate, 10=high OR ☐ = none ▭ = low ◪ = moderate ■ = high

CYCLE DAY	1	2	3	4	5	6	7	8	9	10	11	12	13	14	15	16	17	18	19	20	21	22	23	24	25
Ambition																									
Brainstorming																									
Chattiness																									
Concentration																									
Confidence																									
Courage																									
Creativity																									
Crushes																									
Energy																									
Extroversion																									
Humor/playful																									
Impulsivity																									
Introversion																									
Irritability																									
Libido																									
Memory																									
Money spent																									
Mood: general																									
Optimism																									
Orgasm																									
Patience																									
Productivity																									
Resilience																									
Risk-taking																									
Ruminating																									
Self-image																									
Skepticism																									
Socializing																									
Stress																									
Thinking speed																									
Verbal skills																									
Wanderlust																									
Willpower																									

Mood, Body, Brain

0=none, 1=low, 5=moderate, 10=high OR ☐ = none ◻ = low ◪ = moderate ◼ = high

CYCLE DAY	26	27	28	29	30	31	32	33	34	35	36	37	38	39	40	41	42	43	44	45	46	47	48	49	50
Ambition																									
Brainstorming																									
Chattiness																									
Concentration																									
Confidence																									
Courage																									
Creativity																									
Crushes																									
Energy																									
Extroversion																									
Humor/playful																									
Impulsivity																									
Introversion																									
Irritability																									
Libido																									
Memory																									
Money spent																									
Mood: general																									
Optimism																									
Orgasm																									
Patience																									
Productivity																									
Resilience																									
Risk-taking																									
Ruminating																									
Self-image																									
Skepticism																									
Socializing																									
Stress																									
Thinking speed																									
Verbal skills																									
Wanderlust																									
Willpower																									

Other Mood, Body, Brain

0=none, 1=low, 5=moderate, 10=high OR ☐ = none ▭ = low ◺ = moderate ■ = high

CYCLE DAY	1	2	3	4	5	6	7	8	9	10	11	12	13	14	15	16	17	18	19	20	21	22	23	24	25

NOTES:

Other Mood, Body, Brain

0=none, 1=low, 5=moderate, 10=high OR ☐ = none ▭ = low ◢ = moderate ■ = high

CYCLE DAY	26	27	28	29	30	31	32	33	34	35	36	37	38	39	40	41	42	43	44	45	46	47	48	49	50

NOTES:

_____ to
_____

Menstrual Cycle Tracker #4

Flow: ☐ = none ◉ = spotting ◨ = light ◪ = moderate ◼ = heavy

Cervical Mucus: D = dry, **S** = sticky, **C** = creamy, **W** = watery, **EW** = egg white, ____ = _____

DATE																									
CYCLE DAY	1	2	3	4	5	6	7	8	9	10	11	12	13	14	15	16	17	18	19	20	21	22	23	24	25
Flow/cervical mucus																									
# of products or cup rinses																									
Basal temp																									
Ovulation																									

General Symptoms

0=none, 1=low, 5=moderate, 10=high OR ☐ = none ◨ = low ◪ = moderate ◼ = high

CYCLE DAY	1	2	3	4	5	6	7	8	9	10	11	12	13	14	15	16	17	18	19	20	21	22	23	24	25
Acne																									
Appetite																									
Breast pain																									
Cramps																									
Fatigue																									
Fluid retention																									
Food cravings																									
Gas																									
Headache																									
Migraine																									
Nausea																									
Pain intensity																									
Sadness																									
Sleep issues																									
Stool: hard																									
Stool: loose																									
Urination																									
Worry																									

Menstrual Cycle Tracker #4

Flow: □ = none ⊡ = spotting ◱ = light ◤ = moderate ■ = heavy

Cervical Mucus: D = dry, **S** = sticky, **C** = creamy, **W** = watery, **EW** = egg white, ___ = _____

DATE																									
CYCLE DAY	26	27	28	29	30	31	32	33	34	35	36	37	38	39	40	41	42	43	44	45	46	47	48	49	50
Flow/cervical mucus																									
# of products or cup rinses																									
Basal temp																									
Ovulation																									

General Symptoms

0=none, 1=low, 5=moderate, 10=high OR □ = none ◱ = low ◤ = moderate ■ = high

CYCLE DAY	26	27	28	29	30	31	32	33	34	35	36	37	38	39	40	41	42	43	44	45	46	47	48	49	50
Acne																									
Appetite																									
Breast pain																									
Cramps																									
Fatigue																									
Fluid retention																									
Food cravings																									
Gas																									
Headache																									
Migraine																									
Nausea																									
Pain intensity																									
Sadness																									
Sleep issues																									
Stool: hard																									
Stool: loose																									
Urination																									
Worry																									

Medical Condition Symptoms

0=none, 1=low, 5=moderate, 10=high OR ☐ = none ⬓ = low ◨ = moderate ◼ = high

CYCLE DAY	1	2	3	4	5	6	7	8	9	10	11	12	13	14	15	16	17	18	19	20	21	22	23	24	25
Allergies																									
Anxiety																									
Asthma																									
Depression																									
Dry eye																									
Eczema																									
Endometriosis																									
Epilepsy																									
Fibromyalgia																									
GERD																									
IBS																									
Mania																									
MS																									
OCD																									
PCOS																									
PMDD																									
Social anxiety																									

Other Medical Condition Symptoms

0=none, 1=low, 5=moderate, 10=high OR ☐ = none ⬓ = low ◨ = moderate ◼ = high

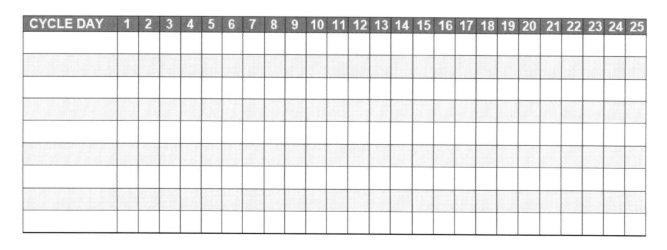

CYCLE DAY	1	2	3	4	5	6	7	8	9	10	11	12	13	14	15	16	17	18	19	20	21	22	23	24	25

Medical Condition Symptoms

0=none, 1=low, 5=moderate, 10=high OR ☐ = none ▭ = low ◪ = moderate ■ = high

CYCLE DAY	26	27	28	29	30	31	32	33	34	35	36	37	38	39	40	41	42	43	44	45	46	47	48	49	50
Allergies																									
Anxiety																									
Asthma																									
Depression																									
Dry eye																									
Eczema																									
Endometriosis																									
Epilepsy																									
Fibromyalgia																									
GERD																									
IBS																									
Mania																									
MS																									
OCD																									
PCOS																									
PMDD																									
Social anxiety																									

Other Medical Condition Symptoms

0=none, 1=low, 5=moderate, 10=high OR ☐ = none ▭ = low ◪ = moderate ■ = high

CYCLE DAY	26	27	28	29	30	31	32	33	34	35	36	37	38	39	40	41	42	43	44	45	46	47	48	49	50

Mood, Body, Brain

0=none, 1=low, 5=moderate, 10=high OR ☐ = none ☐ = low ◪ = moderate ■ = high

CYCLE DAY	1	2	3	4	5	6	7	8	9	10	11	12	13	14	15	16	17	18	19	20	21	22	23	24	25
Ambition																									
Brainstorming																									
Chattiness																									
Concentration																									
Confidence																									
Courage																									
Creativity																									
Crushes																									
Energy																									
Extroversion																									
Humor/playful																									
Impulsivity																									
Introversion																									
Irritability																									
Libido																									
Memory																									
Money spent																									
Mood: general																									
Optimism																									
Orgasm																									
Patience																									
Productivity																									
Resilience																									
Risk-taking																									
Ruminating																									
Self-image																									
Skepticism																									
Socializing																									
Stress																									
Thinking speed																									
Verbal skills																									
Wanderlust																									
Willpower																									

Mood, Body, Brain

0=none, 1=low, 5=moderate, 10=high OR ☐ = none ◨ = low ◪ = moderate ■ = high

CYCLE DAY	26	27	28	29	30	31	32	33	34	35	36	37	38	39	40	41	42	43	44	45	46	47	48	49	50
Ambition																									
Brainstorming																									
Chattiness																									
Concentration																									
Confidence																									
Courage																									
Creativity																									
Crushes																									
Energy																									
Extroversion																									
Humor/playful																									
Impulsivity																									
Introversion																									
Irritability																									
Libido																									
Memory																									
Money spent																									
Mood: general																									
Optimism																									
Orgasm																									
Patience																									
Productivity																									
Resilience																									
Risk-taking																									
Ruminating																									
Self-image																									
Skepticism																									
Socializing																									
Stress																									
Thinking speed																									
Verbal skills																									
Wanderlust																									
Willpower																									

Other Mood, Body, Brain

0=none, 1=low, 5=moderate, 10=high OR ☐ = none ⬜ = low ◪ = moderate ■ = high

CYCLE DAY	1	2	3	4	5	6	7	8	9	10	11	12	13	14	15	16	17	18	19	20	21	22	23	24	25

NOTES:

Other Mood, Body, Brain

0=none, 1=low, 5=moderate, 10=high OR ▢ = none ▭ = low ◹ = moderate ◼ = high

CYCLE DAY	26	27	28	29	30	31	32	33	34	35	36	37	38	39	40	41	42	43	44	45	46	47	48	49	50

NOTES:

Menstrual Cycle Tracker #5

Flow: ☐ = none ⊡ = spotting ◲ = light ◪ = moderate ■ = heavy

Cervical Mucus: D = dry, **S** = sticky, **C** = creamy, **W** = watery, **EW** = egg white, ____ = _____

DATE		1	2	3	4	5	6	7	8	9	10	11	12	13	14	15	16	17	18	19	20	21	22	23	24	25
CYCLE DAY		1	2	3	4	5	6	7	8	9	10	11	12	13	14	15	16	17	18	19	20	21	22	23	24	25
Flow/cervical mucus																										
# of products or cup rinses																										
Basal temp																										
Ovulation																										

General Symptoms

0=none, 1=low, 5=moderate, 10=high OR ☐ = none ◲ = low ◪ = moderate ■ = high

CYCLE DAY	1	2	3	4	5	6	7	8	9	10	11	12	13	14	15	16	17	18	19	20	21	22	23	24	25
Acne																									
Appetite																									
Breast pain																									
Cramps																									
Fatigue																									
Fluid retention																									
Food cravings																									
Gas																									
Headache																									
Migraine																									
Nausea																									
Pain intensity																									
Sadness																									
Sleep issues																									
Stool: hard																									
Stool: loose																									
Urination																									
Worry																									

Menstrual Cycle Tracker #5

Flow: ☐ = none ⊡ = spotting ▄ = light ◪ = moderate ■ = heavy

Cervical Mucus: D = dry, **S** = sticky, **C** = creamy, **W** = watery, **EW** = egg white, ___ = _____

DATE																									
CYCLE DAY	26	27	28	29	30	31	32	33	34	35	36	37	38	39	40	41	42	43	44	45	46	47	48	49	50
Flow/cervical mucus																									
# of products or cup rinses																									
Basal temp																									
Ovulation																									

General Symptoms

0=none, 1=low, 5=moderate, 10=high OR ☐ = none ▄ = low ◪ = moderate ■ = high

CYCLE DAY	26	27	28	29	30	31	32	33	34	35	36	37	38	39	40	41	42	43	44	45	46	47	48	49	50
Acne																									
Appetite																									
Breast pain																									
Cramps																									
Fatigue																									
Fluid retention																									
Food cravings																									
Gas																									
Headache																									
Migraine																									
Nausea																									
Pain intensity																									
Sadness																									
Sleep issues																									
Stool: hard																									
Stool: loose																									
Urination																									
Worry																									

Medical Condition Symptoms

0=none, 1=low, 5=moderate, 10=high OR ☐ = none ◼ = low ◪ = moderate ◼ = high

CYCLE DAY	1	2	3	4	5	6	7	8	9	10	11	12	13	14	15	16	17	18	19	20	21	22	23	24	25
Allergies																									
Anxiety																									
Asthma																									
Depression																									
Dry eye																									
Eczema																									
Endometriosis																									
Epilepsy																									
Fibromyalgia																									
GERD																									
IBS																									
Mania																									
MS																									
OCD																									
PCOS																									
PMDD																									
Social anxiety																									

Other Medical Condition Symptoms

0=none, 1=low, 5=moderate, 10=high OR ☐ = none ◼ = low ◪ = moderate ◼ = high

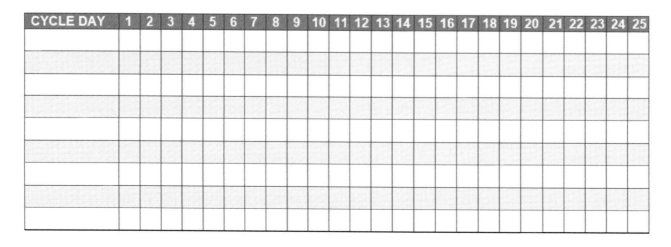

Medical Condition Symptoms

0=none, 1=low, 5=moderate, 10=high OR ☐ = none ▭ = low ◣ = moderate ■ = high

CYCLE DAY	26	27	28	29	30	31	32	33	34	35	36	37	38	39	40	41	42	43	44	45	46	47	48	49	50
Allergies																									
Anxiety																									
Asthma																									
Depression																									
Dry eye																									
Eczema																									
Endometriosis																									
Epilepsy																									
Fibromyalgia																									
GERD																									
IBS																									
Mania																									
MS																									
OCD																									
PCOS																									
PMDD																									
Social anxiety																									

Other Medical Condition Symptoms

0=none, 1=low, 5=moderate, 10=high OR ☐ = none ▭ = low ◣ = moderate ■ = high

CYCLE DAY	26	27	28	29	30	31	32	33	34	35	36	37	38	39	40	41	42	43	44	45	46	47	48	49	50

Mood, Body, Brain

0=none, 1=low, 5=moderate, 10=high OR ☐ = none ⬓ = low ◪ = moderate ■ = high

CYCLE DAY	1	2	3	4	5	6	7	8	9	10	11	12	13	14	15	16	17	18	19	20	21	22	23	24	25
Ambition																									
Brainstorming																									
Chattiness																									
Concentration																									
Confidence																									
Courage																									
Creativity																									
Crushes																									
Energy																									
Extroversion																									
Humor/playful																									
Impulsivity																									
Introversion																									
Irritability																									
Libido																									
Memory																									
Money spent																									
Mood: general																									
Optimism																									
Orgasm																									
Patience																									
Productivity																									
Resilience																									
Risk-taking																									
Ruminating																									
Self-image																									
Skepticism																									
Socializing																									
Stress																									
Thinking speed																									
Verbal skills																									
Wanderlust																									
Willpower																									

Mood, Body, Brain

0=none, 1=low, 5=moderate, 10=high OR ☐ = none ☐ = low ◣ = moderate ◼ = high

CYCLE DAY	26	27	28	29	30	31	32	33	34	35	36	37	38	39	40	41	42	43	44	45	46	47	48	49	50
Ambition																									
Brainstorming																									
Chattiness																									
Concentration																									
Confidence																									
Courage																									
Creativity																									
Crushes																									
Energy																									
Extroversion																									
Humor/playful																									
Impulsivity																									
Introversion																									
Irritability																									
Libido																									
Memory																									
Money spent																									
Mood: general																									
Optimism																									
Orgasm																									
Patience																									
Productivity																									
Resilience																									
Risk-taking																									
Ruminating																									
Self-image																									
Skepticism																									
Socializing																									
Stress																									
Thinking speed																									
Verbal skills																									
Wanderlust																									
Willpower																									

Other Mood, Body, Brain

0=none, 1=low, 5=moderate, 10=high OR ☐ = none ◪ = low ◩ = moderate ◼ = high

CYCLE DAY	1	2	3	4	5	6	7	8	9	10	11	12	13	14	15	16	17	18	19	20	21	22	23	24	25

NOTES:

Other Mood, Body, Brain

0=none, 1=low, 5=moderate, 10=high OR ▢ = none ▢ = low ◪ = moderate ◼ = high

CYCLE DAY	26	27	28	29	30	31	32	33	34	35	36	37	38	39	40	41	42	43	44	45	46	47	48	49	50

NOTES:

Menstrual Cycle Tracker #6

Flow: ☐ = none ◉ = spotting ◪ = light ◩ = moderate ■ = heavy

Cervical Mucus: D = dry, **S** = sticky, **C** = creamy, **W** = watery, **EW** = egg white, ____ = _____

DATE																									
CYCLE DAY	1	2	3	4	5	6	7	8	9	10	11	12	13	14	15	16	17	18	19	20	21	22	23	24	25
Flow/cervical mucus																									
# of products or cup rinses																									
Basal temp																									
Ovulation																									

General Symptoms

0=none, 1=low, 5=moderate, 10=high OR ☐ = none ◪ = low ◩ = moderate ■ = high

CYCLE DAY	1	2	3	4	5	6	7	8	9	10	11	12	13	14	15	16	17	18	19	20	21	22	23	24	25
Acne																									
Appetite																									
Breast pain																									
Cramps																									
Fatigue																									
Fluid retention																									
Food cravings																									
Gas																									
Headache																									
Migraine																									
Nausea																									
Pain intensity																									
Sadness																									
Sleep issues																									
Stool: hard																									
Stool: loose																									
Urination																									
Worry																									

Menstrual Cycle Tracker #6

Flow: ☐ = none ⊡ = spotting ◲ = light ◩ = moderate ■ = heavy

Cervical Mucus: D = dry, **S** = sticky, **C** = creamy, **W** = watery, **EW** = egg white, ___ = _____

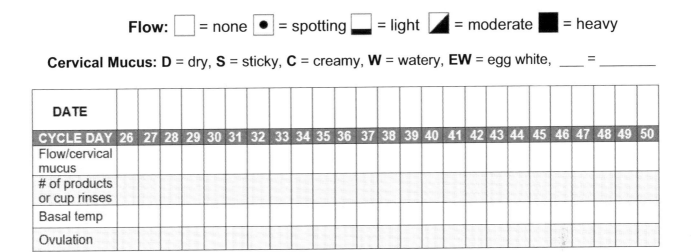

DATE																									
CYCLE DAY	26	27	28	29	30	31	32	33	34	35	36	37	38	39	40	41	42	43	44	45	46	47	48	49	50
Flow/cervical mucus																									
# of products or cup rinses																									
Basal temp																									
Ovulation																									

General Symptoms

0=none, 1=low, 5=moderate, 10=high OR ☐ = none ◲ = low ◩ = moderate ■ = high

CYCLE DAY	26	27	28	29	30	31	32	33	34	35	36	37	38	39	40	41	42	43	44	45	46	47	48	49	50
Acne																									
Appetite																									
Breast pain																									
Cramps																									
Fatigue																									
Fluid retention																									
Food cravings																									
Gas																									
Headache																									
Migraine																									
Nausea																									
Pain intensity																									
Sadness																									
Sleep issues																									
Stool: hard																									
Stool: loose																									
Urination																									
Worry																									

Medical Condition Symptoms

0=none, 1=low, 5=moderate, 10=high OR ☐ = none ⬛ = low ◢ = moderate ⬛ = high

CYCLE DAY	1	2	3	4	5	6	7	8	9	10	11	12	13	14	15	16	17	18	19	20	21	22	23	24	25
Allergies																									
Anxiety																									
Asthma																									
Depression																									
Dry eye																									
Eczema																									
Endometriosis																									
Epilepsy																									
Fibromyalgia																									
GERD																									
IBS																									
Mania																									
MS																									
OCD																									
PCOS																									
PMDD																									
Social anxiety																									

Other Medical Condition Symptoms

0=none, 1=low, 5=moderate, 10=high OR ☐ = none ⬛ = low ◢ = moderate ⬛ = high

CYCLE DAY	1	2	3	4	5	6	7	8	9	10	11	12	13	14	15	16	17	18	19	20	21	22	23	24	25

Medical Condition Symptoms

0=none, 1=low, 5=moderate, 10=high OR ☐ = none ▭ = low ◪ = moderate ■ = high

CYCLE DAY	26	27	28	29	30	31	32	33	34	35	36	37	38	39	40	41	42	43	44	45	46	47	48	49	50
Allergies																									
Anxiety																									
Asthma																									
Depression																									
Dry eye																									
Eczema																									
Endometriosis																									
Epilepsy																									
Fibromyalgia																									
GERD																									
IBS																									
Mania																									
MS																									
OCD																									
PCOS																									
PMDD																									
Social anxiety																									

Other Medical Condition Symptoms

0=none, 1=low, 5=moderate, 10=high OR ☐ = none ▭ = low ◪ = moderate ■ = high

CYCLE DAY	26	27	28	29	30	31	32	33	34	35	36	37	38	39	40	41	42	43	44	45	46	47	48	49	50

Mood, Body, Brain

0=none, 1=low, 5=moderate, 10=high OR ☐ = none ◰ = low ◩ = moderate ◼ = high

CYCLE DAY	1	2	3	4	5	6	7	8	9	10	11	12	13	14	15	16	17	18	19	20	21	22	23	24	25
Ambition																									
Brainstorming																									
Chattiness																									
Concentration																									
Confidence																									
Courage																									
Creativity																									
Crushes																									
Energy																									
Extroversion																									
Humor/playful																									
Impulsivity																									
Introversion																									
Irritability																									
Libido																									
Memory																									
Money spent																									
Mood: general																									
Optimism																									
Orgasm																									
Patience																									
Productivity																									
Resilience																									
Risk-taking																									
Ruminating																									
Self-image																									
Skepticism																									
Socializing																									
Stress																									
Thinking speed																									
Verbal skills																									
Wanderlust																									
Willpower																									

Mood, Body, Brain

0=none, 1=low, 5=moderate, 10=high OR ☐ = none ▭ = low ◣ = moderate ◼ = high

CYCLE DAY	26	27	28	29	30	31	32	33	34	35	36	37	38	39	40	41	42	43	44	45	46	47	48	49	50
Ambition																									
Brainstorming																									
Chattiness																									
Concentration																									
Confidence																									
Courage																									
Creativity																									
Crushes																									
Energy																									
Extroversion																									
Humor/playful																									
Impulsivity																									
Introversion																									
Irritability																									
Libido																									
Memory																									
Money spent																									
Mood: general																									
Optimism																									
Orgasm																									
Patience																									
Productivity																									
Resilience																									
Risk-taking																									
Ruminating																									
Self-image																									
Skepticism																									
Socializing																									
Stress																									
Thinking speed																									
Verbal skills																									
Wanderlust																									
Willpower																									

Other Mood, Body, Brain

0=none, 1=low, 5=moderate, 10=high OR ☐ = none ☐ = low ◤ = moderate ■ = high

CYCLE DAY	1	2	3	4	5	6	7	8	9	10	11	12	13	14	15	16	17	18	19	20	21	22	23	24	25

NOTES:

Other Mood, Body, Brain

0=none, 1=low, 5=moderate, 10=high OR ☐ = none ▭ = low ◪ = moderate ■ = high

CYCLE DAY	26	27	28	29	30	31	32	33	34	35	36	37	38	39	40	41	42	43	44	45	46	47	48	49	50

NOTES:

Menstrual Cycle Tracker #7

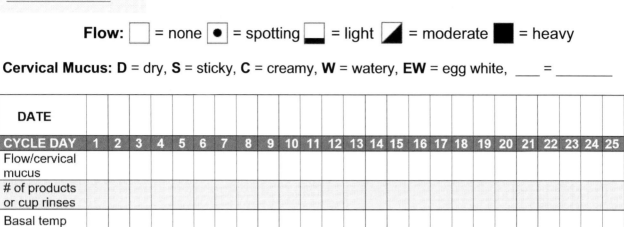

Flow: ☐ = none ☉ = spotting ◩ = light ◪ = moderate ■ = heavy

Cervical Mucus: D = dry, **S** = sticky, **C** = creamy, **W** = watery, **EW** = egg white, ___ = _____

DATE																									
CYCLE DAY	1	2	3	4	5	6	7	8	9	10	11	12	13	14	15	16	17	18	19	20	21	22	23	24	25
Flow/cervical mucus																									
# of products or cup rinses																									
Basal temp																									
Ovulation																									

General Symptoms

0=none, 1=low, 5=moderate, 10=high OR ☐ = none ◩ = low ◪ = moderate ■ = high

CYCLE DAY	1	2	3	4	5	6	7	8	9	10	11	12	13	14	15	16	17	18	19	20	21	22	23	24	25
Acne																									
Appetite																									
Breast pain																									
Cramps																									
Fatigue																									
Fluid retention																									
Food cravings																									
Gas																									
Headache																									
Migraine																									
Nausea																									
Pain intensity																									
Sadness																									
Sleep issues																									
Stool: hard																									
Stool: loose																									
Urination																									
Worry																									

Menstrual Cycle Tracker #7

Flow: ☐ = none ⦿ = spotting ◲ = light ◪ = moderate ◼ = heavy

Cervical Mucus: D = dry, **S** = sticky, **C** = creamy, **W** = watery, **EW** = egg white, ___ = _____

DATE																									
CYCLE DAY	26	27	28	29	30	31	32	33	34	35	36	37	38	39	40	41	42	43	44	45	46	47	48	49	50
Flow/cervical mucus																									
# of products or cup rinses																									
Basal temp																									
Ovulation																									

General Symptoms

0=none, 1=low, 5=moderate, 10=high OR ☐ = none ◲ = low ◪ = moderate ◼ = high

CYCLE DAY	26	27	28	29	30	31	32	33	34	35	36	37	38	39	40	41	42	43	44	45	46	47	48	49	50
Acne																									
Appetite																									
Breast pain																									
Cramps																									
Fatigue																									
Fluid retention																									
Food cravings																									
Gas																									
Headache																									
Migraine																									
Nausea																									
Pain intensity																									
Sadness																									
Sleep issues																									
Stool: hard																									
Stool: loose																									
Urination																									
Worry																									

Medical Condition Symptoms

0=none, 1=low, 5=moderate, 10=high OR ☐ = none ◩ = low ◢ = moderate ■ = high

CYCLE DAY	1	2	3	4	5	6	7	8	9	10	11	12	13	14	15	16	17	18	19	20	21	22	23	24	25
Allergies																									
Anxiety																									
Asthma																									
Depression																									
Dry eye																									
Eczema																									
Endometriosis																									
Epilepsy																									
Fibromyalgia																									
GERD																									
IBS																									
Mania																									
MS																									
OCD																									
PCOS																									
PMDD																									
Social anxiety																									

Other Medical Condition Symptoms

0=none, 1=low, 5=moderate, 10=high OR ☐ = none ◩ = low ◢ = moderate ■ = high

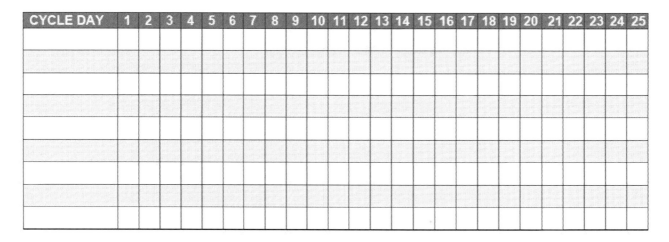

CYCLE DAY	1	2	3	4	5	6	7	8	9	10	11	12	13	14	15	16	17	18	19	20	21	22	23	24	25

Medical Condition Symptoms

0=none, 1=low, 5=moderate, 10=high OR ☐ = none ◪ = low ◣ = moderate ■ = high

CYCLE DAY	26	27	28	29	30	31	32	33	34	35	36	37	38	39	40	41	42	43	44	45	46	47	48	49	50
Allergies																									
Anxiety																									
Asthma																									
Depression																									
Dry eye																									
Eczema																									
Endometriosis																									
Epilepsy																									
Fibromyalgia																									
GERD																									
IBS																									
Mania																									
MS																									
OCD																									
PCOS																									
PMDD																									
Social anxiety																									

Other Medical Condition Symptoms

0=none, 1=low, 5=moderate, 10=high OR ☐ = none ◪ = low ◣ = moderate ■ = high

CYCLE DAY	26	27	28	29	30	31	32	33	34	35	36	37	38	39	40	41	42	43	44	45	46	47	48	49	50

Mood, Body, Brain

0=none, 1=low, 5=moderate, 10=high OR ☐ = none ◻ = low ◨ = moderate ◼ = high

CYCLE DAY	1	2	3	4	5	6	7	8	9	10	11	12	13	14	15	16	17	18	19	20	21	22	23	24	25
Ambition																									
Brainstorming																									
Chattiness																									
Concentration																									
Confidence																									
Courage																									
Creativity																									
Crushes																									
Energy																									
Extroversion																									
Humor/playful																									
Impulsivity																									
Introversion																									
Irritability																									
Libido																									
Memory																									
Money spent																									
Mood: general																									
Optimism																									
Orgasm																									
Patience																									
Productivity																									
Resilience																									
Risk-taking																									
Ruminating																									
Self-image																									
Skepticism																									
Socializing																									
Stress																									
Thinking speed																									
Verbal skills																									
Wanderlust																									
Willpower																									

Mood, Body, Brain

0=none, 1=low, 5=moderate, 10=high OR ☐ = none ◪ = low ◲ = moderate ◼ = high

CYCLE DAY	26	27	28	29	30	31	32	33	34	35	36	37	38	39	40	41	42	43	44	45	46	47	48	49	50
Ambition																									
Brainstorming																									
Chattiness																									
Concentration																									
Confidence																									
Courage																									
Creativity																									
Crushes																									
Energy																									
Extroversion																									
Humor/playful																									
Impulsivity																									
Introversion																									
Irritability																									
Libido																									
Memory																									
Money spent																									
Mood: general																									
Optimism																									
Orgasm																									
Patience																									
Productivity																									
Resilience																									
Risk-taking																									
Ruminating																									
Self-image																									
Skepticism																									
Socializing																									
Stress																									
Thinking speed																									
Verbal skills																									
Wanderlust																									
Willpower																									

Other Mood, Body, Brain

0=none, 1=low, 5=moderate, 10=high OR ☐ = none ▭ = low ◩ = moderate ■ = high

CYCLE DAY	1	2	3	4	5	6	7	8	9	10	11	12	13	14	15	16	17	18	19	20	21	22	23	24	25

NOTES:

Other Mood, Body, Brain

0=none, 1=low, 5=moderate, 10=high OR ☐ = none ▢ = low ◢ = moderate ■ = high

CYCLE DAY	26	27	28	29	30	31	32	33	34	35	36	37	38	39	40	41	42	43	44	45	46	47	48	49	50

NOTES:

Menstrual Cycle Tracker #8

Flow: ☐ = none ⊡ = spotting ▢ = light ◪ = moderate ■ = heavy

Cervical Mucus: D = dry, **S** = sticky, **C** = creamy, **W** = watery, **EW** = egg white, ___ = _____

DATE																									
CYCLE DAY	1	2	3	4	5	6	7	8	9	10	11	12	13	14	15	16	17	18	19	20	21	22	23	24	25
Flow/cervical mucus																									
# of products or cup rinses																									
Basal temp																									
Ovulation																									

General Symptoms

0=none, 1=low, 5=moderate, 10=high OR ☐ = none ▢ = low ◪ = moderate ■ = high

CYCLE DAY	1	2	3	4	5	6	7	8	9	10	11	12	13	14	15	16	17	18	19	20	21	22	23	24	25
Acne																									
Appetite																									
Breast pain																									
Cramps																									
Fatigue																									
Fluid retention																									
Food cravings																									
Gas																									
Headache																									
Migraine																									
Nausea																									
Pain intensity																									
Sadness																									
Sleep issues																									
Stool: hard																									
Stool: loose																									
Urination																									
Worry																									

Menstrual Cycle Tracker #8

Flow: ☐ = none ⊡ = spotting ▭ = light ◪ = moderate ■ = heavy

Cervical Mucus: D = dry, **S** = sticky, **C** = creamy, **W** = watery, **EW** = egg white, ___ = _____

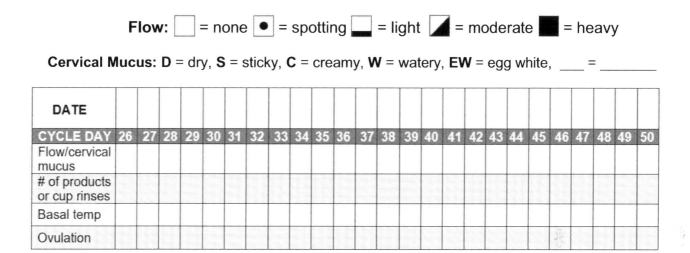

DATE																									
CYCLE DAY	26	27	28	29	30	31	32	33	34	35	36	37	38	39	40	41	42	43	44	45	46	47	48	49	50
Flow/cervical mucus																									
# of products or cup rinses																									
Basal temp																									
Ovulation																									

General Symptoms

0=none, 1=low, 5=moderate, 10=high OR ☐ = none ▭ = low ◪ = moderate ■ = high

CYCLE DAY	26	27	28	29	30	31	32	33	34	35	36	37	38	39	40	41	42	43	44	45	46	47	48	49	50
Acne																									
Appetite																									
Breast pain																									
Cramps																									
Fatigue																									
Fluid retention																									
Food cravings																									
Gas																									
Headache																									
Migraine																									
Nausea																									
Pain intensity																									
Sadness																									
Sleep issues																									
Stool: hard																									
Stool: loose																									
Urination																									
Worry																									

Medical Condition Symptoms

0=none, 1=low, 5=moderate, 10=high OR ☐ = none ▱ = low ◰ = moderate ■ = high

CYCLE DAY	1	2	3	4	5	6	7	8	9	10	11	12	13	14	15	16	17	18	19	20	21	22	23	24	25
Allergies																									
Anxiety																									
Asthma																									
Depression																									
Dry eye																									
Eczema																									
Endometriosis																									
Epilepsy																									
Fibromyalgia																									
GERD																									
IBS																									
Mania																									
MS																									
OCD																									
PCOS																									
PMDD																									
Social anxiety																									

Other Medical Condition Symptoms

0=none, 1=low, 5=moderate, 10=high OR ☐ = none ▱ = low ◰ = moderate ■ = high

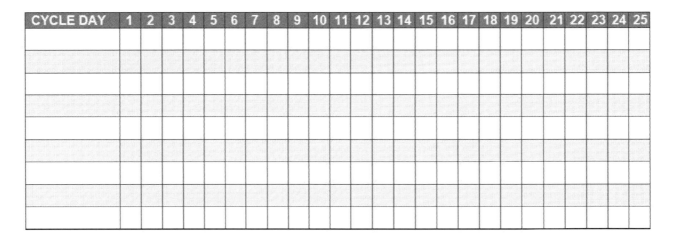

CYCLE DAY	1	2	3	4	5	6	7	8	9	10	11	12	13	14	15	16	17	18	19	20	21	22	23	24	25

Medical Condition Symptoms

0=none, 1=low, 5=moderate, 10=high OR ☐ = none ◺ = low ◣ = moderate ◼ = high

CYCLE DAY	26	27	28	29	30	31	32	33	34	35	36	37	38	39	40	41	42	43	44	45	46	47	48	49	50
Allergies																									
Anxiety																									
Asthma																									
Depression																									
Dry eye																									
Eczema																									
Endometriosis																									
Epilepsy																									
Fibromyalgia																									
GERD																									
IBS																									
Mania																									
MS																									
OCD																									
PCOS																									
PMDD																									
Social anxiety																									

Other Medical Condition Symptoms

0=none, 1=low, 5=moderate, 10=high OR ☐ = none ◺ = low ◣ = moderate ◼ = high

CYCLE DAY	26	27	28	29	30	31	32	33	34	35	36	37	38	39	40	41	42	43	44	45	46	47	48	49	50

Mood, Body, Brain

0=none, 1=low, 5=moderate, 10=high OR ☐ = none ◲ = low ◪ = moderate ◼ = high

CYCLE DAY	1	2	3	4	5	6	7	8	9	10	11	12	13	14	15	16	17	18	19	20	21	22	23	24	25
Ambition																									
Brainstorming																									
Chattiness																									
Concentration																									
Confidence																									
Courage																									
Creativity																									
Crushes																									
Energy																									
Extroversion																									
Humor/playful																									
Impulsivity																									
Introversion																									
Irritability																									
Libido																									
Memory																									
Money spent																									
Mood: general																									
Optimism																									
Orgasm																									
Patience																									
Productivity																									
Resilience																									
Risk-taking																									
Ruminating																									
Self-image																									
Skepticism																									
Socializing																									
Stress																									
Thinking speed																									
Verbal skills																									
Wanderlust																									
Willpower																									

Mood, Body, Brain

0=none, 1=low, 5=moderate, 10=high OR ☐ = none ⬓ = low ◪ = moderate ■ = high

CYCLE DAY	26	27	28	29	30	31	32	33	34	35	36	37	38	39	40	41	42	43	44	45	46	47	48	49	50
Ambition																									
Brainstorming																									
Chattiness																									
Concentration																									
Confidence																									
Courage																									
Creativity																									
Crushes																									
Energy																									
Extroversion																									
Humor/playful																									
Impulsivity																									
Introversion																									
Irritability																									
Libido																									
Memory																									
Money spent																									
Mood: general																									
Optimism																									
Orgasm																									
Patience																									
Productivity																									
Resilience																									
Risk-taking																									
Ruminating																									
Self-image																									
Skepticism																									
Socializing																									
Stress																									
Thinking speed																									
Verbal skills																									
Wanderlust																									
Willpower																									

Other Mood, Body, Brain

0=none, 1=low, 5=moderate, 10=high OR ☐ = none ⬓ = low ◪ = moderate ■ = high

CYCLE DAY	1	2	3	4	5	6	7	8	9	10	11	12	13	14	15	16	17	18	19	20	21	22	23	24	25

NOTES:

Other Mood, Body, Brain

0=none, 1=low, 5=moderate, 10=high OR ☐ = none ◻ = low ◢ = moderate ◼ = high

CYCLE DAY	26	27	28	29	30	31	32	33	34	35	36	37	38	39	40	41	42	43	44	45	46	47	48	49	50

NOTES:

Menstrual Cycle Tracker #9

Flow: ☐ = none ◉ = spotting ◻ = light ◢ = moderate ■ = heavy

Cervical Mucus: D = dry, **S** = sticky, **C** = creamy, **W** = watery, **EW** = egg white, ____ = _____

DATE																									
CYCLE DAY	1	2	3	4	5	6	7	8	9	10	11	12	13	14	15	16	17	18	19	20	21	22	23	24	25
Flow/cervical mucus																									
# of products or cup rinses																									
Basal temp																									
Ovulation																									

General Symptoms

0=none, 1=low, 5=moderate, 10=high OR ☐ = none ◻ = low ◢ = moderate ■ = high

CYCLE DAY	1	2	3	4	5	6	7	8	9	10	11	12	13	14	15	16	17	18	19	20	21	22	23	24	25
Acne																									
Appetite																									
Breast pain																									
Cramps																									
Fatigue																									
Fluid retention																									
Food cravings																									
Gas																									
Headache																									
Migraine																									
Nausea																									
Pain intensity																									
Sadness																									
Sleep issues																									
Stool: hard																									
Stool: loose																									
Urination																									
Worry																									

Menstrual Cycle Tracker #9

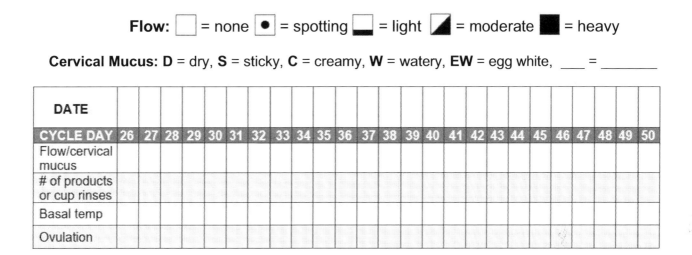

Flow: ☐ = none 🔘 = spotting ◲ = light ◩ = moderate ■ = heavy

Cervical Mucus: D = dry, **S** = sticky, **C** = creamy, **W** = watery, **EW** = egg white, ___ = _____

DATE																									
CYCLE DAY	26	27	28	29	30	31	32	33	34	35	36	37	38	39	40	41	42	43	44	45	46	47	48	49	50
Flow/cervical mucus																									
# of products or cup rinses																									
Basal temp																									
Ovulation																									

General Symptoms

0=none, 1=low, 5=moderate, 10=high OR ☐ = none ◲ = low ◩ = moderate ■ = high

CYCLE DAY	26	27	28	29	30	31	32	33	34	35	36	37	38	39	40	41	42	43	44	45	46	47	48	49	50
Acne																									
Appetite																									
Breast pain																									
Cramps																									
Fatigue																									
Fluid retention																									
Food cravings																									
Gas																									
Headache																									
Migraine																									
Nausea																									
Pain intensity																									
Sadness																									
Sleep issues																									
Stool: hard																									
Stool: loose																									
Urination																									
Worry																									

Medical Condition Symptoms

0=none, 1=low, 5=moderate, 10=high OR ☐ = none ▭ = low ◩ = moderate ■ = high

CYCLE DAY	1	2	3	4	5	6	7	8	9	10	11	12	13	14	15	16	17	18	19	20	21	22	23	24	25
Allergies																									
Anxiety																									
Asthma																									
Depression																									
Dry eye																									
Eczema																									
Endometriosis																									
Epilepsy																									
Fibromyalgia																									
GERD																									
IBS																									
Mania																									
MS																									
OCD																									
PCOS																									
PMDD																									
Social anxiety																									

Other Medical Condition Symptoms

0=none, 1=low, 5=moderate, 10=high OR ☐ = none ▭ = low ◩ = moderate ■ = high

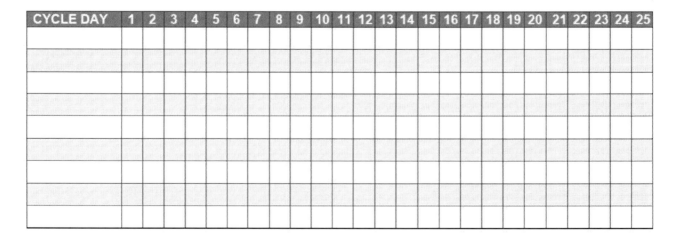

Medical Condition Symptoms

0=none, 1=low, 5=moderate, 10=high OR ☐ = none ⬚ = low ◨ = moderate ■ = high

CYCLE DAY	26	27	28	29	30	31	32	33	34	35	36	37	38	39	40	41	42	43	44	45	46	47	48	49	50
Allergies																									
Anxiety																									
Asthma																									
Depression																									
Dry eye																									
Eczema																									
Endometriosis																									
Epilepsy																									
Fibromyalgia																									
GERD																									
IBS																									
Mania																									
MS																									
OCD																									
PCOS																									
PMDD																									
Social anxiety																									

Other Medical Condition Symptoms

0=none, 1=low, 5=moderate, 10=high OR ☐ = none ⬚ = low ◨ = moderate ■ = high

CYCLE DAY	26	27	28	29	30	31	32	33	34	35	36	37	38	39	40	41	42	43	44	45	46	47	48	49	50

Mood, Body, Brain

0=none, 1=low, 5=moderate, 10=high OR ☐ = none ◻ = low ◪ = moderate ◼ = high

CYCLE DAY	1	2	3	4	5	6	7	8	9	10	11	12	13	14	15	16	17	18	19	20	21	22	23	24	25
Ambition																									
Brainstorming																									
Chattiness																									
Concentration																									
Confidence																									
Courage																									
Creativity																									
Crushes																									
Energy																									
Extroversion																									
Humor/playful																									
Impulsivity																									
Introversion																									
Irritability																									
Libido																									
Memory																									
Money spent																									
Mood: general																									
Optimism																									
Orgasm																									
Patience																									
Productivity																									
Resilience																									
Risk-taking																									
Ruminating																									
Self-image																									
Skepticism																									
Socializing																									
Stress																									
Thinking speed																									
Verbal skills																									
Wanderlust																									
Willpower																									

Mood, Body, Brain

0=none, 1=low, 5=moderate, 10=high OR ☐ = none ☐ = low ◪ = moderate ■ = high

CYCLE DAY	26	27	28	29	30	31	32	33	34	35	36	37	38	39	40	41	42	43	44	45	46	47	48	49	50
Ambition																									
Brainstorming																									
Chattiness																									
Concentration																									
Confidence																									
Courage																									
Creativity																									
Crushes																									
Energy																									
Extroversion																									
Humor/playful																									
Impulsivity																									
Introversion																									
Irritability																									
Libido																									
Memory																									
Money spent																									
Mood: general																									
Optimism																									
Orgasm																									
Patience																									
Productivity																									
Resilience																									
Risk-taking																									
Ruminating																									
Self-image																									
Skepticism																									
Socializing																									
Stress																									
Thinking speed																									
Verbal skills																									
Wanderlust																									
Willpower																									

Other Mood, Body, Brain

0=none, 1=low, 5=moderate, 10=high OR ☐ = none ⬓ = low ◹ = moderate ■ = high

CYCLE DAY	1	2	3	4	5	6	7	8	9	10	11	12	13	14	15	16	17	18	19	20	21	22	23	24	25

NOTES:

Other Mood, Body, Brain

0=none, 1=low, 5=moderate, 10=high OR ☐ = none ◻ = low ◢ = moderate ■ = high

CYCLE DAY	26	27	28	29	30	31	32	33	34	35	36	37	38	39	40	41	42	43	44	45	46	47	48	49	50

NOTES:

Menstrual Cycle Tracker #10

Flow: ☐ = none ⦿ = spotting ◲ = light ◥ = moderate ■ = heavy

Cervical Mucus: D = dry, **S** = sticky, **C** = creamy, **W** = watery, **EW** = egg white, ____ = _____

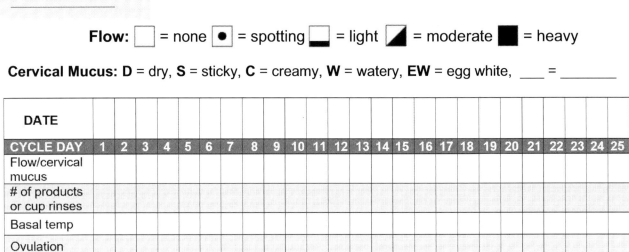

DATE																									
CYCLE DAY	1	2	3	4	5	6	7	8	9	10	11	12	13	14	15	16	17	18	19	20	21	22	23	24	25
Flow/cervical mucus																									
# of products or cup rinses																									
Basal temp																									
Ovulation																									

General Symptoms

0=none, 1=low, 5=moderate, 10=high OR ☐ = none ◲ = low ◥ = moderate ■ = high

CYCLE DAY	1	2	3	4	5	6	7	8	9	10	11	12	13	14	15	16	17	18	19	20	21	22	23	24	25
Acne																									
Appetite																									
Breast pain																									
Cramps																									
Fatigue																									
Fluid retention																									
Food cravings																									
Gas																									
Headache																									
Migraine																									
Nausea																									
Pain intensity																									
Sadness																									
Sleep issues																									
Stool: hard																									
Stool: loose																									
Urination																									
Worry																									

Menstrual Cycle Tracker #10

Flow: ☐ = none ⊡ = spotting ◲ = light ◰ = moderate ■ = heavy

Cervical Mucus: D = dry, **S** = sticky, **C** = creamy, **W** = watery, **EW** = egg white, _____ = _____

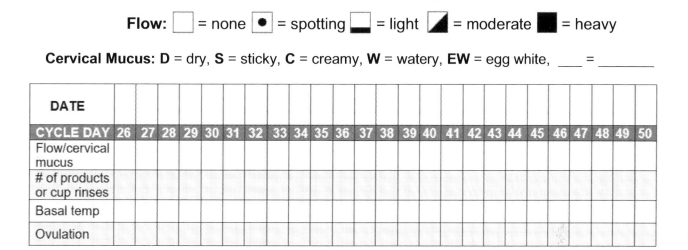

DATE																									
CYCLE DAY	26	27	28	29	30	31	32	33	34	35	36	37	38	39	40	41	42	43	44	45	46	47	48	49	50
Flow/cervical mucus																									
# of products or cup rinses																									
Basal temp																									
Ovulation																									

General Symptoms

0=none, 1=low, 5=moderate, 10=high OR ☐ = none ◲ = low ◰ = moderate ■ = high

CYCLE DAY	26	27	28	29	30	31	32	33	34	35	36	37	38	39	40	41	42	43	44	45	46	47	48	49	50
Acne																									
Appetite																									
Breast pain																									
Cramps																									
Fatigue																									
Fluid retention																									
Food cravings																									
Gas																									
Headache																									
Migraine																									
Nausea																									
Pain intensity																									
Sadness																									
Sleep issues																									
Stool: hard																									
Stool: loose																									
Urination																									
Worry																									

Medical Condition Symptoms

0=none, 1=low, 5=moderate, 10=high OR ☐ = none ◻ = low ◢ = moderate ■ = high

CYCLE DAY	1	2	3	4	5	6	7	8	9	10	11	12	13	14	15	16	17	18	19	20	21	22	23	24	25
Allergies																									
Anxiety																									
Asthma																									
Depression																									
Dry eye																									
Eczema																									
Endometriosis																									
Epilepsy																									
Fibromyalgia																									
GERD																									
IBS																									
Mania																									
MS																									
OCD																									
PCOS																									
PMDD																									
Social anxiety																									

Other Medical Condition Symptoms

0=none, 1=low, 5=moderate, 10=high OR ☐ = none ◻ = low ◢ = moderate ■ = high

CYCLE DAY	1	2	3	4	5	6	7	8	9	10	11	12	13	14	15	16	17	18	19	20	21	22	23	24	25

Medical Condition Symptoms

0=none, 1=low, 5=moderate, 10=high OR ☐ = none ◻ = low ◢ = moderate ■ = high

CYCLE DAY	26	27	28	29	30	31	32	33	34	35	36	37	38	39	40	41	42	43	44	45	46	47	48	49	50
Allergies																									
Anxiety																									
Asthma																									
Depression																									
Dry eye																									
Eczema																									
Endometriosis																									
Epilepsy																									
Fibromyalgia																									
GERD																									
IBS																									
Mania																									
MS																									
OCD																									
PCOS																									
PMDD																									
Social anxiety																									

Other Medical Condition Symptoms

0=none, 1=low, 5=moderate, 10=high OR ☐ = none ◻ = low ◢ = moderate ■ = high

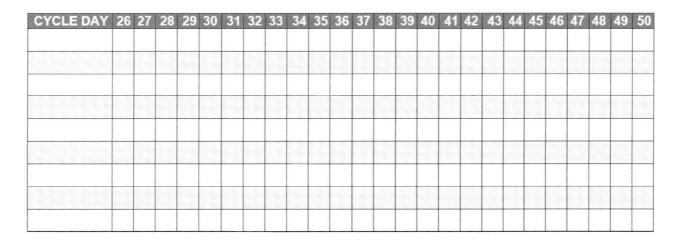

CYCLE DAY	26	27	28	29	30	31	32	33	34	35	36	37	38	39	40	41	42	43	44	45	46	47	48	49	50

Mood, Body, Brain

0=none, 1=low, 5=moderate, 10=high OR ☐ = none ◻ = low ◩ = moderate ■ = high

CYCLE DAY	1	2	3	4	5	6	7	8	9	10	11	12	13	14	15	16	17	18	19	20	21	22	23	24	25
Ambition																									
Brainstorming																									
Chattiness																									
Concentration																									
Confidence																									
Courage																									
Creativity																									
Crushes																									
Energy																									
Extroversion																									
Humor/playful																									
Impulsivity																									
Introversion																									
Irritability																									
Libido																									
Memory																									
Money spent																									
Mood: general																									
Optimism																									
Orgasm																									
Patience																									
Productivity																									
Resilience																									
Risk-taking																									
Ruminating																									
Self-image																									
Skepticism																									
Socializing																									
Stress																									
Thinking speed																									
Verbal skills																									
Wanderlust																									
Willpower																									

Mood, Body, Brain

0=none, 1=low, 5=moderate, 10=high OR ☐ = none ◪ = low ◩ = moderate ■ = high

CYCLE DAY	26	27	28	29	30	31	32	33	34	35	36	37	38	39	40	41	42	43	44	45	46	47	48	49	50
Ambition																									
Brainstorming																									
Chattiness																									
Concentration																									
Confidence																									
Courage																									
Creativity																									
Crushes																									
Energy																									
Extroversion																									
Humor/playful																									
Impulsivity																									
Introversion																									
Irritability																									
Libido																									
Memory																									
Money spent																									
Mood: general																									
Optimism																									
Orgasm																									
Patience																									
Productivity																									
Resilience																									
Risk-taking																									
Ruminating																									
Self-image																									
Skepticism																									
Socializing																									
Stress																									
Thinking speed																									
Verbal skills																									
Wanderlust																									
Willpower																									

Other Mood, Body, Brain

0=none, 1=low, 5=moderate, 10=high OR ☐ = none ▬ = low ◿ = moderate ■ = high

CYCLE DAY	1	2	3	4	5	6	7	8	9	10	11	12	13	14	15	16	17	18	19	20	21	22	23	24	25

NOTES:

Other Mood, Body, Brain

0=none, 1=low, 5=moderate, 10=high OR ☐ = none ◻ = low ◩ = moderate ■ = high

CYCLE DAY	26	27	28	29	30	31	32	33	34	35	36	37	38	39	40	41	42	43	44	45	46	47	48	49	50

NOTES:

Menstrual Cycle Tracker #11

Flow: ☐ = none ⊡ = spotting ◻ = light ◪ = moderate ■ = heavy

Cervical Mucus: D = dry, **S** = sticky, **C** = creamy, **W** = watery, **EW** = egg white, ____ = _____

DATE																									
CYCLE DAY	1	2	3	4	5	6	7	8	9	10	11	12	13	14	15	16	17	18	19	20	21	22	23	24	25
Flow/cervical mucus																									
# of products or cup rinses																									
Basal temp																									
Ovulation																									

General Symptoms

0=none, 1=low, 5=moderate, 10=high OR ☐ = none ◻ = low ◪ = moderate ■ = high

CYCLE DAY	1	2	3	4	5	6	7	8	9	10	11	12	13	14	15	16	17	18	19	20	21	22	23	24	25
Acne																									
Appetite																									
Breast pain																									
Cramps																									
Fatigue																									
Fluid retention																									
Food cravings																									
Gas																									
Headache																									
Migraine																									
Nausea																									
Pain intensity																									
Sadness																									
Sleep issues																									
Stool: hard																									
Stool: loose																									
Urination																									
Worry																									

Menstrual Cycle Tracker #11

Flow: ☐ = none ⊡ = spotting ◱ = light ◪ = moderate ■ = heavy

Cervical Mucus: **D** = dry, **S** = sticky, **C** = creamy, **W** = watery, **EW** = egg white, ____ = _____

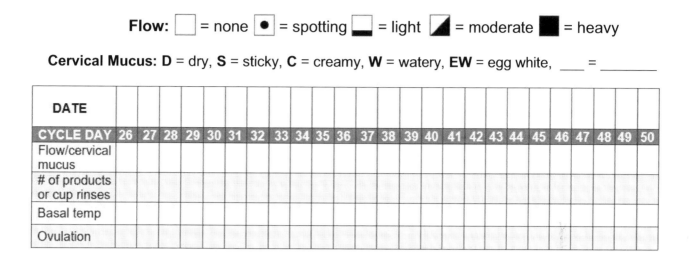

DATE																									
CYCLE DAY	26	27	28	29	30	31	32	33	34	35	36	37	38	39	40	41	42	43	44	45	46	47	48	49	50
Flow/cervical mucus																									
# of products or cup rinses																									
Basal temp																									
Ovulation																									

General Symptoms

0=none, 1=low, 5=moderate, 10=high OR ☐ = none ◱ = low ◪ = moderate ■ = high

CYCLE DAY	26	27	28	29	30	31	32	33	34	35	36	37	38	39	40	41	42	43	44	45	46	47	48	49	50
Acne																									
Appetite																									
Breast pain																									
Cramps																									
Fatigue																									
Fluid retention																									
Food cravings																									
Gas																									
Headache																									
Migraine																									
Nausea																									
Pain intensity																									
Sadness																									
Sleep issues																									
Stool: hard																									
Stool: loose																									
Urination																									
Worry																									

Medical Condition Symptoms

0=none, 1=low, 5=moderate, 10=high OR ☐ = none ▭ = low ◸ = moderate ■ = high

CYCLE DAY	1	2	3	4	5	6	7	8	9	10	11	12	13	14	15	16	17	18	19	20	21	22	23	24	25
Allergies																									
Anxiety																									
Asthma																									
Depression																									
Dry eye																									
Eczema																									
Endometriosis																									
Epilepsy																									
Fibromyalgia																									
GERD																									
IBS																									
Mania																									
MS																									
OCD																									
PCOS																									
PMDD																									
Social anxiety																									

Other Medical Condition Symptoms

0=none, 1=low, 5=moderate, 10=high OR ☐ = none ▭ = low ◸ = moderate ■ = high

CYCLE DAY	1	2	3	4	5	6	7	8	9	10	11	12	13	14	15	16	17	18	19	20	21	22	23	24	25

Medical Condition Symptoms

0=none, 1=low, 5=moderate, 10=high OR ☐ = none ▭ = low ◩ = moderate ■ = high

CYCLE DAY	26	27	28	29	30	31	32	33	34	35	36	37	38	39	40	41	42	43	44	45	46	47	48	49	50
Allergies																									
Anxiety																									
Asthma																									
Depression																									
Dry eye																									
Eczema																									
Endometriosis																									
Epilepsy																									
Fibromyalgia																									
GERD																									
IBS																									
Mania																									
MS																									
OCD																									
PCOS																									
PMDD																									
Social anxiety																									

Other Medical Condition Symptoms

0=none, 1=low, 5=moderate, 10=high OR ☐ = none ▭ = low ◩ = moderate ■ = high

CYCLE DAY	26	27	28	29	30	31	32	33	34	35	36	37	38	39	40	41	42	43	44	45	46	47	48	49	50

Mood, Body, Brain

0=none, 1=low, 5=moderate, 10=high OR ☐ = none ◪ = low ◪ = moderate ◼ = high

CYCLE DAY	1	2	3	4	5	6	7	8	9	10	11	12	13	14	15	16	17	18	19	20	21	22	23	24	25
Ambition																									
Brainstorming																									
Chattiness																									
Concentration																									
Confidence																									
Courage																									
Creativity																									
Crushes																									
Energy																									
Extroversion																									
Humor/playful																									
Impulsivity																									
Introversion																									
Irritability																									
Libido																									
Memory																									
Money spent																									
Mood: general																									
Optimism																									
Orgasm																									
Patience																									
Productivity																									
Resilience																									
Risk-taking																									
Ruminating																									
Self-image																									
Skepticism																									
Socializing																									
Stress																									
Thinking speed																									
Verbal skills																									
Wanderlust																									
Willpower																									

Mood, Body, Brain

0=none, 1=low, 5=moderate, 10=high OR ☐ = none ◻ = low ◩ = moderate ■ = high

CYCLE DAY	26	27	28	29	30	31	32	33	34	35	36	37	38	39	40	41	42	43	44	45	46	47	48	49	50
Ambition																									
Brainstorming																									
Chattiness																									
Concentration																									
Confidence																									
Courage																									
Creativity																									
Crushes																									
Energy																									
Extroversion																									
Humor/playful																									
Impulsivity																									
Introversion																									
Irritability																									
Libido																									
Memory																									
Money spent																									
Mood: general																									
Optimism																									
Orgasm																									
Patience																									
Productivity																									
Resilience																									
Risk-taking																									
Ruminating																									
Self-image																									
Skepticism																									
Socializing																									
Stress																									
Thinking speed																									
Verbal skills																									
Wanderlust																									
Willpower																									

Other Mood, Body, Brain

0=none, 1=low, 5=moderate, 10=high OR ☐ = none ▭ = low ◩ = moderate ■ = high

CYCLE DAY	1	2	3	4	5	6	7	8	9	10	11	12	13	14	15	16	17	18	19	20	21	22	23	24	25

NOTES:

Other Mood, Body, Brain

0=none, 1=low, 5=moderate, 10=high OR ☐ = none ◳ = low ◣ = moderate ■ = high

CYCLE DAY	26	27	28	29	30	31	32	33	34	35	36	37	38	39	40	41	42	43	44	45	46	47	48	49	50

NOTES:

Menstrual Cycle Tracker #12

Flow: ☐ = none ⊡ = spotting ◪ = light ◩ = moderate ■ = heavy

Cervical Mucus: D = dry, **S** = sticky, **C** = creamy, **W** = watery, **EW** = egg white, ____ = _____

DATE																									
CYCLE DAY	1	2	3	4	5	6	7	8	9	10	11	12	13	14	15	16	17	18	19	20	21	22	23	24	25
Flow/cervical mucus																									
# of products or cup rinses																									
Basal temp																									
Ovulation																									

General Symptoms

0=none, 1=low, 5=moderate, 10=high OR ☐ = none ◪ = low ◩ = moderate ■ = high

CYCLE DAY	1	2	3	4	5	6	7	8	9	10	11	12	13	14	15	16	17	18	19	20	21	22	23	24	25
Acne																									
Appetite																									
Breast pain																									
Cramps																									
Fatigue																									
Fluid retention																									
Food cravings																									
Gas																									
Headache																									
Migraine																									
Nausea																									
Pain intensity																									
Sadness																									
Sleep issues																									
Stool: hard																									
Stool: loose																									
Urination																									
Worry																									

Menstrual Cycle Tracker #12

Flow: ☐ = none ◉ = spotting ◱ = light ◪ = moderate ■ = heavy

Cervical Mucus: D = dry, **S** = sticky, **C** = creamy, **W** = watery, **EW** = egg white, ____ = _____

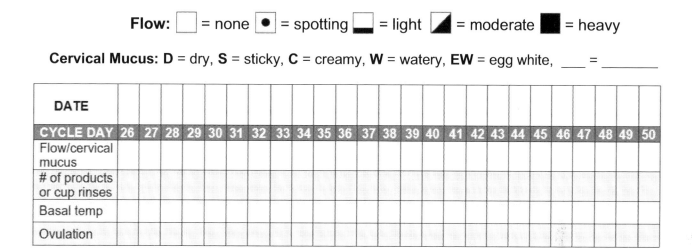

DATE																									
CYCLE DAY	26	27	28	29	30	31	32	33	34	35	36	37	38	39	40	41	42	43	44	45	46	47	48	49	50
Flow/cervical mucus																									
# of products or cup rinses																									
Basal temp																									
Ovulation																									

General Symptoms

0=none, 1=low, 5=moderate, 10=high OR ☐ = none ◱ = low ◪ = moderate ■ = high

CYCLE DAY	26	27	28	29	30	31	32	33	34	35	36	37	38	39	40	41	42	43	44	45	46	47	48	49	50
Acne																									
Appetite																									
Breast pain																									
Cramps																									
Fatigue																									
Fluid retention																									
Food cravings																									
Gas																									
Headache																									
Migraine																									
Nausea																									
Pain intensity																									
Sadness																									
Sleep issues																									
Stool: hard																									
Stool: loose																									
Urination																									
Worry																									

Medical Condition Symptoms

0=none, 1=low, 5=moderate, 10=high OR ☐ = none ▢ = low ◪ = moderate ■ = high

CYCLE DAY	1	2	3	4	5	6	7	8	9	10	11	12	13	14	15	16	17	18	19	20	21	22	23	24	25
Allergies																									
Anxiety																									
Asthma																									
Depression																									
Dry eye																									
Eczema																									
Endometriosis																									
Epilepsy																									
Fibromyalgia																									
GERD																									
IBS																									
Mania																									
MS																									
OCD																									
PCOS																									
PMDD																									
Social anxiety																									

Other Medical Condition Symptoms

0=none, 1=low, 5=moderate, 10=high OR ☐ = none ▢ = low ◪ = moderate ■ = high

CYCLE DAY	1	2	3	4	5	6	7	8	9	10	11	12	13	14	15	16	17	18	19	20	21	22	23	24	25

Medical Condition Symptoms

0=none, 1=low, 5=moderate, 10=high OR ☐ = none ⬛ = low ◢ = moderate ■ = high

CYCLE DAY	26	27	28	29	30	31	32	33	34	35	36	37	38	39	40	41	42	43	44	45	46	47	48	49	50
Allergies																									
Anxiety																									
Asthma																									
Depression																									
Dry eye																									
Eczema																									
Endometriosis																									
Epilepsy																									
Fibromyalgia																									
GERD																									
IBS																									
Mania																									
MS																									
OCD																									
PCOS																									
PMDD																									
Social anxiety																									

Other Medical Condition Symptoms

0=none, 1=low, 5=moderate, 10=high OR ☐ = none ⬛ = low ◢ = moderate ■ = high

CYCLE DAY	26	27	28	29	30	31	32	33	34	35	36	37	38	39	40	41	42	43	44	45	46	47	48	49	50

Mood, Body, Brain

0=none, 1=low, 5=moderate, 10=high OR ☐ = none ◻ = low ◢ = moderate ■ = high

CYCLE DAY	1	2	3	4	5	6	7	8	9	10	11	12	13	14	15	16	17	18	19	20	21	22	23	24	25
Ambition																									
Brainstorming																									
Chattiness																									
Concentration																									
Confidence																									
Courage																									
Creativity																									
Crushes																									
Energy																									
Extroversion																									
Humor/playful																									
Impulsivity																									
Introversion																									
Irritability																									
Libido																									
Memory																									
Money spent																									
Mood: general																									
Optimism																									
Orgasm																									
Patience																									
Productivity																									
Resilience																									
Risk-taking																									
Ruminating																									
Self-image																									
Skepticism																									
Socializing																									
Stress																									
Thinking speed																									
Verbal skills																									
Wanderlust																									
Willpower																									

Mood, Body, Brain

0=none, 1=low, 5=moderate, 10=high OR ☐ = none ▄ = low ◸ = moderate ■ = high

CYCLE DAY	26	27	28	29	30	31	32	33	34	35	36	37	38	39	40	41	42	43	44	45	46	47	48	49	50
Ambition																									
Brainstorming																									
Chattiness																									
Concentration																									
Confidence																									
Courage																									
Creativity																									
Crushes																									
Energy																									
Extroversion																									
Humor/playful																									
Impulsivity																									
Introversion																									
Irritability																									
Libido																									
Memory																									
Money spent																									
Mood: general																									
Optimism																									
Orgasm																									
Patience																									
Productivity																									
Resilience																									
Risk-taking																									
Ruminating																									
Self-image																									
Skepticism																									
Socializing																									
Stress																									
Thinking speed																									
Verbal skills																									
Wanderlust																									
Willpower																									

Other Mood, Body, Brain

0=none, 1=low, 5=moderate, 10=high OR ☐ = none ▭ = low ◪ = moderate ■ = high

CYCLE DAY	1	2	3	4	5	6	7	8	9	10	11	12	13	14	15	16	17	18	19	20	21	22	23	24	25

NOTES:

Other Mood, Body, Brain

0=none, 1=low, 5=moderate, 10=high OR ☐ = none ☐ = low ◢ = moderate ■ = high

CYCLE DAY	26	27	28	29	30	31	32	33	34	35	36	37	38	39	40	41	42	43	44	45	46	47	48	49	50

NOTES:

About the Author

Gabrielle Lichterman pioneered the cycle-syncing and hormone awareness movement in 2005 with the first edition of her groundbreaking book, ***28 Days: What Your Cycle Reveals About Your Moods, Health and Potential***.

She's the founder of **Hormonology**®—an educational outreach mission that teaches women and girls how hormones impact their moods, health and behavior every day of their cycle. She's also the creator of the popular suite of **Hormone Horoscope** apps for women and teen girls and the **Female Forecaster** app for male partners of cycling women.

Gabrielle is recognized as a leading expert in how cycling hormones impact the brain and body and is a widely-respected women's health journalist who has been at the forefront of covering women's issues for more than 20 years. Her articles have appeared in dozens of major publications around the globe, including *CosmoGirl*, *First for Women*, *Glamour*, *Marie Claire*, *New York Daily News*, *Self*, *Woman's World* and *Working Mother*.

Learn more about Gabrielle and her Hormonology mission at MyHormonology.com.

(f) /hormonology

(◎) @hormonology

(🐦) @hormonology

(▶) /hormonology

Printed in Great Britain
by Amazon

10071986R00104